CARE AND SHARE
A Book About Manners

By Rita Golden Gelman   Illustrated by Cathy Beylon

MARVEL BOOKS

CARE AND SHARE
A Book About Manners

When ninety-five friends
Come over to play.

And they all want to swing.
And they all want to stay,
They're in a big mess
Until everyone learns
That in order to swing…

They have to take turns.

If you have an elephant-friend with a cold.
And she doesn't know much
cause she's not very old.

If she coughs 20 times
And she still isn't through.

If her red nose is stuffed
and her eyes are red, too

If she takes a deep breath
and gets ready to sneeze

Hand her a tissue and say
"Use it Please."

On Monday the chimpanzees
Borrowed your glue,
Your bike and your doll
And your book about Pooh.

On Tuesday they came to your door
And they said,
"We used up the glue
And the doll has no head.
The bike has a scratch
And the book has a tear.
Now we'd like to come in
And see what else is there."

"I'm angry," you say.
"You can't come any more."
Then you take all your toys
And you lock-up the door.

They can't come today.
And they can't come tomorrow.
Unless…

they take care of the
things that they borrow.

Your flight was terrific.
You're in a good mood.

And then you find out
You've forgotten your food.

If a troopful of tigers
Comes out of the trees,
And they say to you,
"Eat with us. Eat with us, please."

Then they serve you some
spiders and beetles and such.
Be *sure* you say,

"Thank you. Thank you so much!"

You have batted your ball
Right over the wall
And it lands in a picnic of bears.
You quickly run over
To get your ball back
And you're greeted by grumbles and stares

The ball has ruined their blueberry pie.
It has muddled their chicken and cheese.
A word of advice:...
Be especially nice...

Don't forget to say sorry and please.

If your friends like to eat
And invite you to lunch,
And they stuff all the food
In their mouths in a bunch,
Then they stuff in some more
And they talk while they do,

Say to them,

"Please close your mouths when you chew."

You want to give up,
But you don't; you refuse.
You're determined to learn
How to tie your own shoes.

After twenty-five hours,
You've finally learned it.
Your mother says,
"Here is a cookie.
You've earned it!"

And just at that second,
Why who should appear?
It's your very best friend.
And she's standing right there.

You really don't want to.
You know it's not fair.
But a friend is a friend
  is a friend,
So…

you share.